TRAIN YOUR BRAIN

THINK
LIKE A
CODER

written by Alex Woolf

illustrated by David Broadbent

WAYLAND
www.waylandbooks.co.uk

First published in Great Britain in 2021 by Wayland
Copyright © Hodder and Stoughton, 2021

Produced for Wayland by
White-Thomson Publishing Ltd
www.wtpub.co.uk

Series Designer: David Broadbent
All Illustrations by: David Broadbent

Every attempt has been made to clear copyright. Should there be any
inadvertent omission please apply to the publisher for rectification.

Printed in China

Wayland
An imprint of
Hachette Children's Group
Part of Hodder & Stoughton
Carmelite House
50 Victoria Embankment
London EC4Y 0DZ

An Hachette UK Company
www.hachettechildrens.co.uk

The activities described in this
book should always be done in the
presence of a trusted adult.
A trusted adult is a person (over
18 years old) in a child's life who
makes them feel safe, comfortable
and supported. It might be
a parent, teacher, family friend,
care worker or another adult.

Facts, figures and dates were correct when going to press.

A note from the author and publisher
In preparation of this book, all due care has been exercised with regard to the instructions, activities
and techniques depicted. The publishers and author regret that they can accept no liability for any
loss or injury sustained. Always get adult supervision and follow manufacturers' advice when using
electric and battery-powered appliances.

Every effort has been made by the Publishers to ensure websites are suitable for children, that they
are of the highest educational value, and that they contain no inappropriate or offensive material.
However, because of the nature of the Internet, it is impossible to guarantee that the contents of these
sites will not be altered. We strongly advise that Internet access is supervised by a responsible adult.

CONTENTS

Could You Be a Coder?

Have you ever wondered how computers do what they do?
When you ask a search engine for today's weather,
or when you push a button and a game character
moves on your screen, how does it happen?
Is the computer thinking
for itself?

> No,
> I don't think so ...

The computer is following
a set of instructions written by a **coder.**

The coder writes these instructions in a special
language that a computer can understand.

```
<def> es x *:- [0]i(as):C
- <title>
post'=%s"}at
else:
=%(nodename):[]
forin name=app
<meta ="descrip"/>
```

It might seem like a strange kind of
language because it is made of numbers,
symbols and odd words.

If you can learn and write the
language of computers, you'll
become a coder, and you'll be
much in demand. Coders create
the games we play on our
devices, the websites we visit,
and all our favourite social media
and video-sharing **apps.**

If you learn to code, you could get a job in the world of technology, creating the programs we use every day on our devices, or writing code for the machines that contain computers. Kitchen appliances, alarm clocks, smart TVs, traffic lights, cars and lifts – coders write the instructions that control all these things. They even write the code that tells robots on Mars what to do.

Move forward ...

Stop ...

Take photo ...

Send to Earth ...

Do you like the idea of being a coder? Do you want to be the person who writes the instructions that tell computers how to perform their tasks?

If so, read this book and begin to train your brain to think like a coder.

Learn to Speak Computer

The first thing you have to understand about communicating with computers is that there are really only two things a computer understands: 1 and 0.

Every computer contains billions of tiny devices called **transistors**. These are switches that control the flow of an electric current.

When the switch is on, the electric current can flow. In computer language, on is represented as 1.

1

0

When the switch is off, the electric current is blocked. In computer language, off is represented as 0.

This system of ones and zeroes is called **binary code** (also known as **machine code**) and it's the most basic of computer languages.

But writing in binary code is very slow!

So coders use **programming languages**.

Programming languages are closer to normal human language than binary and much quicker to write. The computer converts the programming language into binary in order to understand it.

Every piece of data a computer receives is recorded as either a zero or a one, and this is called a **bit**. A group of eight bits is called a **byte**. A byte is the smallest unit of digital data. Each letter of the alphabet, for example, is represented as a byte.

Here are the capital letters of the alphabet in binary:

A	01000001		
B	01000010		
C	01000011		
D	01000100		
E	01000101	N	01001110
F	01000110	O	01001111
G	01000111	P	01010000
H	01001000	Q	01010001
I	01001001	R	01010010
J	01001010	S	01010011
K	01001011	T	01010100
L	01001100	U	01010101
M	01001101	V	01010110
		W	01010111
		X	01011000
		Y	01011001
		Z	01011010

Try writing your name in binary.

Be Precise

Communicating with a computer is nothing like talking to a friend. When we speak English, we often use phrases that everyone understands, but that would confuse a computer.

It's not rocket science!

Learning to code will be a piece of cake!

Computers are highly **logical**. A piece of code can only ever mean one thing. There's no room for doubt.

So to be a coder, you need to learn to communicate in a completely different way from the way you communicate with your fellow humans. You need to be very **precise**.

You have to make sure you use the right characters, symbols and spaces. If you miss out just one piece of code, such as **(**, **"**, **{** or **IF**, the computer won't understand you and won't know what you want it to do.

Being precise isn't always easy, because code, when you first look at it, looks a lot like gibberish!

To see some code, go to any website and click **CTRL+U** if you're on a PC, or **Option+Command+U** if you're on a Mac.

That's the source code of the web page you're looking at.
It tells your computer what the web page should look like and contain.

Do you want to try doing some simple coding yourself?
Go to this website and follow the instructions on the screen:

www.crunchzilla.com/code-monster

Play around with the coding to move and change the size of the boxes.

Notice that if you make a small mistake, such as typing a letter instead of a number, the computer won't understand the instruction.

So type carefully and try to be precise!

Ada Lovelace: Computer Pioneer

Ada was a pioneer of computing, though she lived a century before the dawn of the computer age. She was born on 10 December 1815, in London, England. Her father, the famous poet Lord Byron, abandoned his family when Ada was a month old. Her mother, Anne Milbanke, was a highly intelligent woman, skilled in mathematics and science.

In Ada's day, most girls didn't go to school. But Anne was wealthy enough to afford private tutors, and Ada received a high-quality education. When Ada was 17, she met Charles Babbage, Lucasian Professor of Mathematics at the University of Cambridge. Ada was fascinated to hear that Babbage was developing a steam-driven calculating machine called the difference engine. She asked him to send her the designs, so she could see how the machine worked.

In 1837, Babbage began work on a new project – the **analytical engine**. This would be the first programmable computer. Ada's interest was caught when she read a paper about it, written in French. She translated the paper into English, adding her own notes. Ada's version turned out to be three times longer than the original paper!

In her paper, Ada used mathematics to show how the analytical engine could perform calculations. She also included the world's first **algorithm**, or set of instructions for a computer. The algorithm would have programmed the analytical engine to compute a series of numbers called Bernouille Numbers. For this reason, Ada is often called the world's first computer programmer, although it is fair to say that Babbage's work influenced her ideas.

Ada was the first person to realise that the analytical engine could go beyond pure calculation. She understood that anything could be converted into numbers and she predicted that one day computers might perform other roles, such as composing music.

Ada became a pioneer of computers because she had three important qualities: logical skills, discipline and the imagination to see the potential of what she had created. Babbage called her 'an enchantress of numbers'. Ada Lovelace died at the age of 36, on 27 November 1852.

Analytical engine

Be Creative

Coding isn't just about writing code – it's also about being creative. Coders write computer programs to solve problems and to make life easier and more enjoyable. That means engaging the creative side of your brain.

How do I think creatively?

Why not start by trying to think of a problem you want to solve? What sort of things frustrate you about the world that could be solved by a new computer app? What could make your life better or more convenient?

In order to decide on what program to write, you need to find out what users want. Talk to your friends about what they most enjoy doing on a computer.

There's a way you can think creatively and have fun at the same time.

Play a video game – the more complex the better. As you play, list all your favourite things about it, then all the things you'd like to improve.

To organise your thoughts, break your analysis down into separate categories:

Story and character development: does it have an entertaining, emotional storyline, with engaging characters?

Gameplay: is it difficult enough to challenge you? Is there enough variety? Are the choices interesting? Are the combats too repetitive?

Replay value: is it the sort of game you would want to go back to time and again?

To think like a coder, try to imagine things you could do to improve the games you play.

Have Fun

To be a coder, you'll need to learn a **programming language**. Just like learning any foreign language, this will take time and persistence.

Phew! This is hard work!

If you approach it the right way, it doesn't have to be THAT hard.

First of all, choose one of the simpler programming languages, and one that's right for your needs. The easiest languages to start on are:

Python – for websites, mobile apps and games

JavaScript – for creating interactive elements on web pages, games and mobile apps

Java – for websites, mobile apps and games

HTML – for creating web pages   **Ruby** – for websites

When you start learning, why not turn the process into a competition with yourself? Set yourself daily targets and see if you can beat them. Quiz yourself about what you've learned.

Try learning with a friend – it's always more fun that way.

The more time you spend on
a programming language, the quicker you'll learn it,
so try and find time to practise once a day.

Learning any new skill is like building up a special muscle in your
brain. As with any muscle, you need to work on it regularly. Once
you've learned one programming language, it'll be easier to learn others.

Learning to code can seem daunting, but by changing the way
you think about it, you can make the whole process a lot more enjoyable.

Finally, remember why you're doing it. Think of all the brilliant
things you can do once you've learned how to code.

Break It Down

A big part of coding is understanding how computers 'think'. Of course computers aren't really thinking – they are manipulating zeroes and ones according to a set of instructions. As a result, computers may sometimes seem very simple-minded to us.

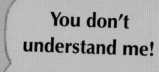
You don't understand me!

Computers can't make big leaps of understanding. So when you write code, you need to take a task that would be extremely simple for a human to understand and break it down into very small steps.

If someone asked you to draw a picture of a house, you'd say:

That's easy!

But a computer would need to understand what paper is, what a pencil is and how to hold it and how hard to press. That's before we've even explained to it what a house is!

When you come to a staircase, most people don't think twice about how to walk up it. Now imagine trying to program a robot to walk up the same staircase. We have to break the task down. Your first instruction might be …

Place your left foot on the first step.

But the robot might just detach its left foot from its leg and place it on the step. You didn't tell it not to! Also, how does the robot know how high the first step is? Your instructions will need to include a measurement of the height of the step.

Think of another simple task, such as making a sandwich or putting on a pair of shoes.

This is quite a fun activity to do with a friend. Your friend can play the part of the computer. They should listen to your words carefully and do exactly what you say, even if this wasn't what you intended.

Learn the Rules

Like human languages, programming languages have their own rules, called **syntax**. These state how you must set out the words and symbols. The rules aren't that different from language to language, so once you've mastered one set, you'll find others easier to learn.

Don't worry about learning all the rules before you start coding.

That would be boring!

It's best to learn a few rules, then get started. Coding is a practical skill – a bit like playing the violin. The sooner you get stuck in, the quicker you'll learn.

Coding isn't a series of facts you memorise, it's a skill you learn, and the only way to learn it is to do it over and over again.

We all have different ways of learning.

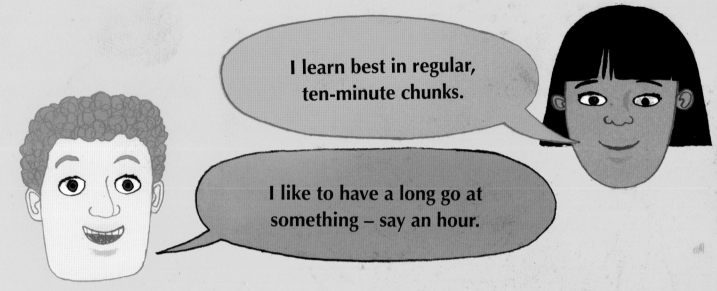

I learn best in regular, ten-minute chunks.

I like to have a long go at something – say an hour.

Some people are better at learning in a group, while others learn better alone. Work out a way of learning to code that suits you and your brain.

If you hit a problem, don't worry. Have an Internet browser open on your screen, so you can look things up as you go.

Don't worry, I'm quite easy to grasp.

Are you ready to get started? Visit w3schools.com. Here you will find tutorials on languages, such as **Python**.

Read the tutorials and have a go at some of the exercises.

Grace Hopper: Early Programmer

Computer pioneer Grace Hopper was born in New York City, USA, on 9 December 1906. She studied mathematics and physics at college, and in 1934 earned a PhD in mathematics at Yale University – one of the first women to do so.

After the US entered the Second World War in 1941, Grace enlisted in the US Naval Reserve and became a lieutenant. She joined a team at Harvard University working on an early computer called the Mark I, making top-secret calculations vital to the war effort. They worked out things like the path of a flying missile and the range of anti-aircraft guns.

After the war, Grace stayed at Harvard where she worked on more advanced computers, the Mark II and Mark III. She helped popularise the term 'bug', meaning a computer error, after a moth flew into the Mark II, causing an electrical fault. 'First actual case of bug being found,' Grace wrote in her diary.

In 1952, Grace wrote the first **compiler**, a program that translates mathematical code into machine code (binary). This was an important step in the development of modern programming languages.

Grace was passionate about encouraging non-mathematicians to embrace computers. In 1953, she suggested the idea of writing a computer program in words rather than mathematical symbols. Experts told her the idea wouldn't work, but Grace persisted, and in 1956 her team wrote FLOW-MATIC, the first programming language to use regular English words. In 1959, she was part of the team that developed COBOL, the world's first widely used programming language.

Aged 60, Grace returned to the navy, where she continued her work in computer languages. Nicknamed 'Amazing Grace' by her colleagues, she finally retired in 1986, aged 79.

Grace Hopper died aged 85 on 1 January 1992. She may have trained as a mathematician, but what made her a great coder was the way she inspired non-mathematicians to get involved in computers. By pioneering the use of ordinary language in programming, Grace helped open up computers to a much wider community of users.

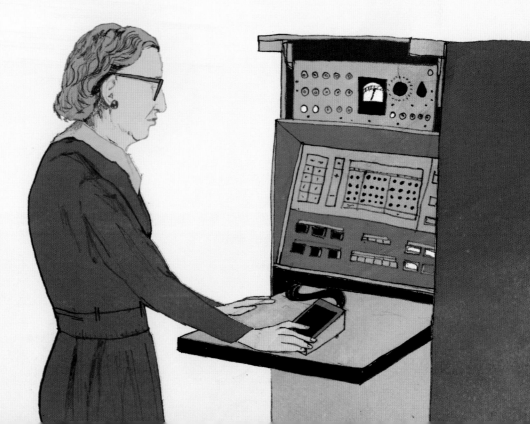

Be Logical

To think like a coder, you need to use **logic**. That might sound difficult, but don't worry, you're already using logic all the time without thinking about it. We use logic every time we employ the **if-then** formula: 'IF this happens, **THEN** do that'. For example, **IF** cold, **THEN** put on jumper. **IF** tired, **THEN** sleep. In logic, this is called a conditional statement.

You can use the **if-then** formula in coding when you want to allow more than one pathway through a program. Say you're writing a program to encourage people to exercise more, the coding could include the instruction:

IF thirsty, THEN drink water.

IF person remains still for more than an hour, THEN print: 'Get moving!'

The **if-then** formula can be expanded to include **else**, meaning 'otherwise'.
So in a program that offers people pleasant greetings,
the coding could include:

IF time is before 12 noon, **THEN** print: 'Good morning!'

IF time is after 6 pm, **THEN** print: 'Good evening!'

ELSE print: 'Good afternoon!'

This can be shown as a flow chart.

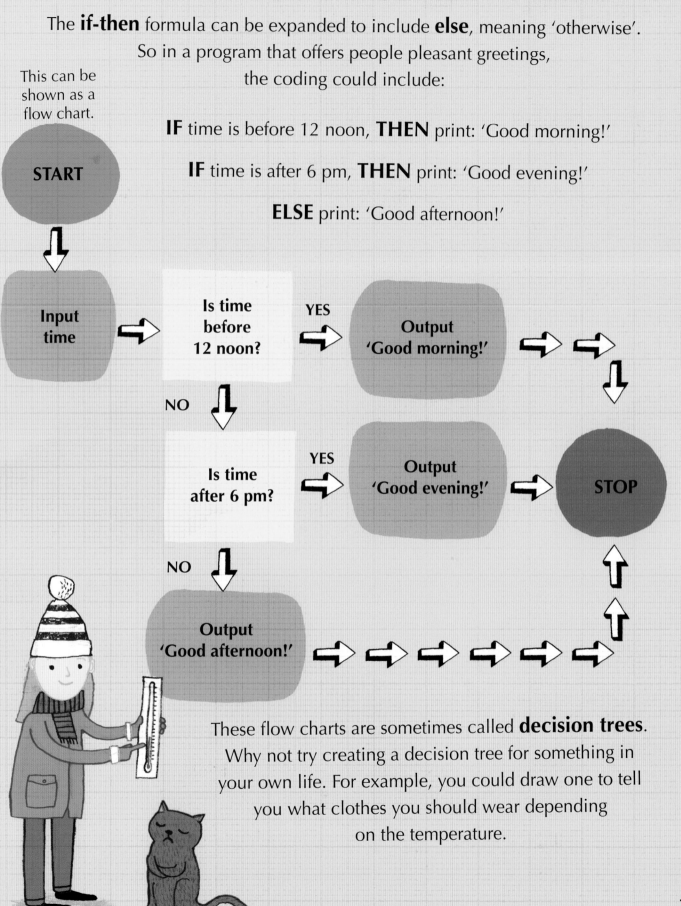

These flow charts are sometimes called **decision trees**.
Why not try creating a decision tree for something in
your own life. For example, you could draw one to tell
you what clothes you should wear depending
on the temperature.

Don't Worry

If you're feeling a little daunted by the idea of learning to code, don't worry. You're not alone. Lots of people feel that way when they're starting out. Maybe you've said to yourself ...

I can't do this!

It's okay. This is a common feeling whenever we try something new. But remember, as you grow up, your brain is constantly developing. What seems difficult today may seem easy in the future.

Luckily, coding has never been easier than it is today. There are plenty of online **tutorials** and **forums** where your questions can be answered.

If you get stuck, help is always just a few clicks away.

Also, programming languages are much simpler to learn and write than they used to be. You don't even have to know what every part of the code does – only that it works.

Will you make mistakes?
Of course you will. We all do.
Part of the fun of coding is working out what you did wrong and putting it right. That's one of the ways that we learn.

So next time you make a mistake, don't get angry with yourself. See it as a learning opportunity.

And most of all, don't worry! Think about what comes naturally to you now – it might be singing, cycling, baking or playing chess. Remember, you were once a beginner at all those things, too.

If you learned those skills, you can master coding, too!

Watch Out for Bugs

Nobody's perfect. We all make mistakes when we write code. These mistakes are called **bugs**. Finding them and fixing them is a big part of learning to be a coder!

What's an example of a bug?

Where are you, bug?

Say you're playing a game and you want the rabbit to go forwards when you press the arrow key, but it goes backwards, that's because of a bug.

Computer programs can contain millions of lines of code, so it's hardly surprising that they contain bugs. A big part of your job as a coder is to run tests on the program to find the bugs and get rid of them, so it runs smoothly.

This is called **debugging**.

Even after the program is finished, you'll need to continually monitor it. Some bugs stay hidden for a long time.

Bugs are a problem,
but they can also be seen as a challenge
and part of the fun of coding. First you have to
work out what kind of problem it is. Then you have
to find it – this is usually the most time-consuming
part. Finally, you need to fix it.

If you're hunting through your code for a bug, don't get
too stressed. The first thing coders always learn in these
situations is to **stay calm**.

You know there's an error buried in there somewhere and
you will find it eventually. So why not treat it as a
treasure hunt. Or imagine you're a detective
searching for clues at a crime scene.

Go through your code line by line and don't
give up until you root out your error.

Bill Gates: Microsoft Founder

Bill Gates was born on 28 October 1955 in Seattle, Washington, USA. He was a competitive child who did well at school, especially in science and maths. His first experience with computers came when he was 13 and he joined his school's computer club. Bill was amazed at what a computer could do and spent many hours working on it. He wrote a program that allowed students to play noughts and crosses with the computer.

Bill's best friend was Paul Allen and the two of them spent much of their free time in the computer lab writing programs in a language called BASIC. When they were 15, the boys started their own business. In 1973, Bill enrolled at Harvard University to study law, but he continued writing programs with Paul, including one for a new personal computer called the Altair.

The software (programs and data used by a computer) they made for the Altair was a success. Together, they founded a company called Microsoft. By 1979 the company was worth $2.5 million. Bill personally reviewed every line of code the company created and often rewrote it if he thought it necessary.

Bill was a very clever businessman. He made sure that Microsoft kept ownership of the software they created. Big computer companies like IBM wanted to buy the code, but Bill refused to sell it. That way, Microsoft earned money every time a computer was sold. Paul Allen left the company in 1983, leaving Bill in sole charge. As personal computers (PCs) became more popular in the 1980s, Microsoft went from strength to strength. By 1983, around 30 per cent of the world's computers ran on its software. By 1990, Bill was among the world's wealthiest individuals.

In 2000, Bill stepped down from day-to-day running of Microsoft to spend more time on the Bill and Melinda Gates Foundation, a charitable organisation that he runs with his wife Melinda, dedicated to supporting healthcare, reducing poverty and expanding educational opportunities around the world.

Bill Gates found success only partly because of his coding abilities. He also had imagination and vision. He correctly foresaw a time when there would be a personal computer on every office desk and in every home, and he set about creating the software that would be key to this computing revolution.

Be Accurate

When you send a text message to a friend, you can make the odd mistake and they'll still understand what you're saying. Computers can't do that. So when you're coding, you have to be accurate.

If you make a spelling mistake in a piece of code, or you mistype a character or a symbol, it creates a bug in the program. This type of bug is called a **syntax bug**. Even the tiniest error can cause one.

HOW
TO
SPELL

So, in a game where you want a knight to fight a dragon, it won't work if you spell *knight* as *night*.

Or if you want an elf to listen to a tale, it's no good if you spell it *tail*. This could cause the program to crash or not run at all.

Fixing syntax errors is easy. Finding them is harder. A common syntax error is leaving out a speech mark or bracket. So if you see one of these, check its pair is there, too.

There are two errors in this piece of Python code. Can you spot them? The answer is below.

```python
patient = input("Enter patient's name: ")

  doctor = input"Enter doctor's name: ")

time = input("Enter the appointment time: ")

print(doctor, "will see", patiant, "at", time)
```

Remember: the more accurate you are, the less time you'll need to spend later hunting for bugs.

So when you're coding, don't work fast – work accurately!

Answer:
There's a missing bracket in line 2, and patient is spelled incorrectly in line 4. Here is the correct version:

```python
patient = input("Enter patient's name: ")
doctor = input("Enter doctor's name: ")
time = input("Enter the appointment time: ")
print(doctor, "will see", patient, "at", time)
```

Watch Your Steps

Imagine you're playing a video game and you're trying to escape from an evil mouse. However hard you try to get away, the mouse always catches you, no matter what. You could be having a nightmare – or maybe the game has a ...

Logical bug!

Logical bugs are caused by an error in logic. This isn't like a syntax bug. The coding is correct and the program works – but it works in a different way from the way the coder intended.

The best way to understand logical bugs is to think of coding as writing a recipe – a series of steps you must follow to prepare something.

All the steps have to be there and correct for the recipe to work. If the steps are in the wrong order, if a step gives the wrong instruction, or if a step is repeated or has been missed out, it can cause a logical bug.

Here is a recipe for a cheese sandwich with logical bugs in it.
Can you work out what might go wrong?

1. Take slice of bread and spread butter on it.

2. Take second slice of bread and spread butter on it.

3. Place second slice of bread on top of first slice of bread.

4. Cut bread into four triangles.

5. Take slice of cheese and place on first slice of bread.

Can you write a recipe without any logical bugs in it?

Be Organised

Coding can be great fun. It can also be really frustrating. Either way, it can take up hours and hours of your day. For the sake of your mental and physical health, you shouldn't let it take over your life. You can avoid this by being **organised** in the way you live and work.

I must finish this!

Here are a few tips for how to organise your coding life.

Instead of getting angry or frustrated when a program goes wrong or crashes, give yourself a **checklist of common errors**. Each time you finish a piece of coding, run through the checklist to make sure you haven't made any obvious mistakes.

As you learn, keep a list of useful techniques or short cuts,
so you can refer back to it in future.

Set yourself goals for what you want to achieve and by when.

Organise your day with a schedule.
Include time for coding
among all your other
activities. Make sure
you stick to it.

**Do at least an hour of exercise a day.
You'll come back fresher and more productive!**

Don't code when you're tired
– that's when you're most likely
to make mistakes. Some people
are slow-starters in the morning
or get sleepy after meals.
Work out when your brain is at its
sharpest and do your coding then.

Take regular breaks from the computer –
5 to 10 minutes every hour.

You could try to focus on your breathing
for 10 to 20 minutes a day. It can really
help your concentration.

Be a Team Player

Coding can seem like a solitary activity – just a person on their own in front of a screen. But today, most coding is done in teams. So to think like a coder, you need to be able to work with other people. You need to be a **team player**.

She works. I sleep. What a team!

For example, coders work in teams to create video games, with different people working on the concept, setting, characters, art and story.

To work as a team, you need certain skills. You have to be able to:

- communicate your thoughts and ideas
- listen to other people
- give and receive feedback
- show respect to other members of the team
- agree or disagree with them respectfully
- accept that they will sometimes disagree with you.

Here's a teambuilding activity you can try.
It needs a minimum of six people,
plus four scarves and a long rope.

Four members of the team must volunteer
to tie scarves around their heads,
covering their eyes so they can't see.

Each of the blindfolded ones are gently
spun around and must then find part of
the rope, pick it up and form a square.
The non-blindfolded ones can help
them, but only by using words.

This exercise may seem very different from
coding, but it teaches two important skills
needed by coding teams: communication
and cooperation.

Remember, everyone in the team is there for the same
reason. You share responsibility for the project you're
working on and you all want it to be a success.

Tim Berners Lee: Web Inventor

Imagine life without the **World Wide Web**. Someone had to come up with the idea and the man who did so was Tim Berners Lee. He didn't invent the **Internet** itself – that's been around since the 1960s – but by creating the World Wide Web (WWW), he turned the Internet into a tool that anyone could use.

Tim was born in London, UK, on 8 June 1955. He studied Physics at Oxford University and graduated with top marks in 1976. Later, he went to work at CERN, the European Organisation for Nuclear Research, in Geneva, Switzerland.

In 1989, while at CERN, Tim came up with his incredible idea. He proposed that scientists all over the world would be able to communicate and share information over the Internet using a system called **hypertext**. Hypertext is computer text that contains links to other texts. He named this global network of interlinked computers the World Wide Web.

Tim began work on the project in 1990. He created the first **web browser**, and on 6 August 1991 he launched the world's first website – **http://info.cern.ch.** Tim and his team invented **HTTP** (HyperText Transfer Protocol), a system of rules governing the sending of files over the Internet. Tim also created **HTML**, a system for tagging text files so they can be displayed on the WWW as web pages. These innovations made the WWW a practical possibility.

Before Tim built the WWW, the Internet was only used by universities and the military, and there were just a few thousand computers on the network. Thanks to the WWW, and Tim's selfless determination to keep it free, the Internet took off all around the world. Today there are around two billion websites.

In 1994, Tim founded the World Wide Web Consortium (W3C), an international community of experts that work together to develop the rules of the WWW. In 2008, he founded the World Wide Web Foundation, an organisation devoted to keeping the Web a free, open, shared resource for everyone.

Through his skill, vision and selfless attitude, Tim Berners Lee created something that has revolutionised the world.

Find Flaws

Coders create the software that makes computers work. They also help protect that software. Coders called **hackers** try to hack into computer systems. Criminal hackers may do this to steal money or information. Some good hackers try to stop them.

These good hackers look for flaws and weaknesses in computer systems. They do this by trying to hack in themselves.

If they manage to hack into a computer system, they alert the owners, and the problem is fixed.

This makes computers more secure, so criminals will find it harder to break into them.

To beat the criminal hackers, you need to be good at coding and problem-solving. You also need to be able to think like a criminal hacker, so you can imagine the devious techniques they might use.

It's not just big companies that can get hacked. Personal accounts can, too. Stay safe online. Remember the 5 P's:

- **Passwords:** use strong ones with letters, numbers and symbols, don't share them with anyone, change them regularly and don't use the same password for everything

- **Privacy settings:** control who sees what information about you

- **Personal information:** don't give your name, phone number or address to people you don't know

- **Profile:** make sure people can't work out much about you from your profile

- **Padlock:** Before you enter private information such as payment or address details into a website, make sure there's a padlock symbol in the browser address bar – that means it's secure.

Ask For Help

Coding is a lot of fun, but it can also be a real headache when you run into problems. People love to share their knowledge, so if you're struggling with something, ask your friends about it. Get them to check your code in case they can see where you went wrong.

Where did I go wrong?

If your friends can't help, try asking the experts. Post your question in a **forum**. The coding community is very friendly and happy to share its knowledge. Remember to make your question specific, not general. Don't just ask ...

How do I do this?'

Ask this kind of question ...

I tried A and expected B, but got C. What's going on?

Tell them the operating system you're using, and the programming language. Include a sample of the code that's causing you problems, and any error messages you received.

When asking for help, be patient. Coders are busy people. When someone replies with a suggestion, try it out and feed back what works and what doesn't. Once you've found a solution, share it with the community so that others can benefit from your experience.

Asking for help can be embarrassing. You may think of it as a sign that you've failed. In fact, it's a sign that you're determined to learn and improve. Every coder in the world was once a beginner who needed help. If you keep practising, one day, people may come to you for help!

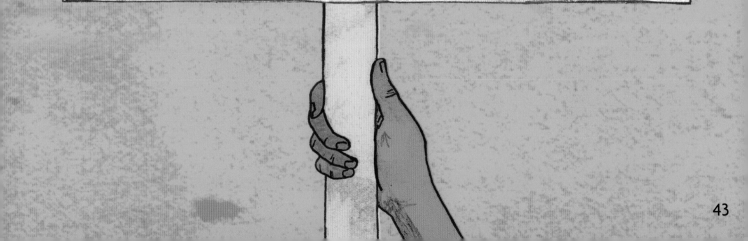

Get Practising

To become successful at anything, you need to practise. With coding, practising is especially important because it's a practical skill, like riding a bike. So don't spend too much time reading about it or watching tutorials. Get on that keyboard, download a code editor and start writing your own little programs.

Practice makes Purr-fect! Right, Tiddles?

With practice, little and often is usually the best approach. So make sure you practise for a short period – no more than an hour – every day.
Very soon you'll notice the improvement.

Focus on one programming language to start with and don't move onto the next until you've mastered that one.

I'm already getting faster and more accurate!

When you first learn to code, you focus on the technical stuff: the syntax, the symbols and the logic. Everything seems unfamiliar and you worry about making mistakes.

With practice, the technical stuff becomes more natural, and you'll start to get creative and original in your coding.

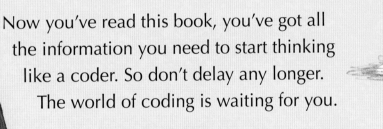

Make coding your hobby. The more you enjoy it, the more you'll want to do it, and the more ambitious you'll be to try new things, like building an app or a website. Once you've finished a project, upload it. Ask your family and friends to use it and send you feedback.

Now you've read this book, you've got all the information you need to start thinking like a coder. So don't delay any longer. The world of coding is waiting for you.

Glossary

algorithm a set of rules to be followed by a computer in order to perform a calculation or solve a problem

app an application program, or piece of software designed for a particular purpose – especially one used on a mobile device such as a smart phone

bernouille numbers a sequence of numbers, useful to mathematicians, discovered by Swiss mathematician Jacob Bernouille

browser a computer program used for accessing information on the World Wide Web

code editor a piece of software designed for writing and editing code

debugging identifying and removing errors from a computer program

forum a web page where users can post comments about a particular topic

hacker a coder who uses computers to gain access to data, or someone employed to stop them

Internet a global network of computers that allows people to communicate and share information

logic a way of thinking that uses reason to work out, for example, whether something is true or false

logical bug an error that allows a computer to carry out its instructions, but not in a way the coder intended.

machine code a language that a computer can understand

operating system the software that supports a computer's basic functions and keeps everything working

programming language a language coders use to write programs, which a computer converts into machine code in order to understand

software the programs and operating system used by a computer. This is often compared to the hardware, which is the physical machinery of a computer.

symbol a character that isn't a letter or number, such as @, which is used to represent something, for example in a computer language

syntax the set of rules that define how a programming language should be structured

syntax bug a spelling or syntax error in a programming language that causes the program to crash or not run at all

transistor a device used in computers that controls the flow of an electric current

World Wide Web a system on the Internet that allows web pages to be connected to other web pages through a browser so that users can search for information by moving from one web page to another

Further information

Books

A World of Computers and Coding by Clive Gifford (Wayland, 2019)
This book tells you all about the history of computers and coding. It explains how computers work, and shows you how you can be a coder yourself with step-by-step instructions to program your own computer game.

Code: STEM (series) by Max Wainewright (Wayland, 2019)
Each book in this series looks at a different technology, be it robots, smart homes, space tech or transport, and explains the computer coding behind them. Step-by-step activities teach you how to create your own versions of these machines on screen, using code.

Ready, Steady, Code! (series) by Álvaro Scrivano (Wayland, 2018–20)
This easy-to-use series is full of projects and tips to get you programming. It includes titles on Hopscotch, Python, Scratch Jr and Minecraft.

Generation Code (series) by Max Wainewright (Wayland, 2018–19)
This series trains you in the coding languages used by real-world computer programmers. It includes titles on Scratch, Python, HTML, app development and JavaScript.

Websites

https://www.bbc.co.uk/bitesize/topics/zvsc7ty
This website from the BBC is a helpful introduction to coding, full of information, games and videos. There are sections on algorithms, computers, computer bugs, computer games and robots.

https://codeclub.org/en/
A global network of free coding clubs for children. The website includes easy-to-follow, step-by-step guides to learning Scratch, HTML/CSS and Python while creating your own games, animations and websites.

https://code.org/
A great resource containing free coding courses and activities for kids of all ages.
It helps you code your own art, stories, games and apps.

https://scratch.mit.edu/
Scratch is a special programming language aimed at kids of 8 to 16.
There are no difficult lines of code to master. Instead you arrange and snap together Scratch blocks. It allows you to build stories, games and animations and share these with others in the global Scratch community.

Index

TRAIN YOUR BRAIN

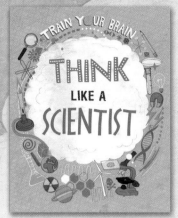

THINK LIKE A SCIENTIST

978 1 5263 1644 8 (HB)
978 1 5263 1645 5 (PB)

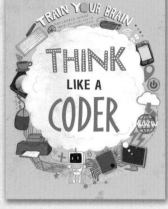

THINK LIKE A CODER

978 1 5263 1650 9 (HB)
978 1 5263 1651 6 (PB)

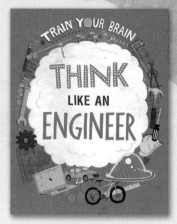

THINK LIKE AN ENGINEER

978 1 5263 1652 3 (HB)
978 1 5263 1653 0 (PB)

THINK LIKE AN ARTIST

978 1 5263 1654 7 (HB)
978 1 5263 1655 4 (PB)

THINK LIKE A MATHEMATICIAN

978 1 5263 1656 1 (HB)
978 1 5263 1657 8 (PB)

THINK LIKE AN ASTRONAUT

978 1 5263 1658 5 (HB)
978 1 5263 1659 2 (PB)

Series contents

Think Like a Scientist
- Are You Curious?
- Collect Data
- Marie Curie
- The Scientific Method
- Ask a Question
- Try a Hypothesis
- Test it Out
- Galileo Galilei
- Dig into the Data
- Mistakes are OK!
- Make a Model
- Star Seekers
- Debra Fischer
- Fossil Finders
- Weather Wizards
- Learn about Life
- That Lightbulb Moment
- Garrett Morgan
- Mending Minds
- Super Scientists
- Change the World

Think Like A Coder
- Could you be a Coder?
- Learn to Speak Computer
- Be Precise
- Ada Lovelace
- Be Creative
- Have Fun
- Break it Down
- Learn the Rules
- Grace Hopper
- Be Logical
- Don't Worry
- Watch Out for Bugs
- Bill Gates
- Be Accurate
- Watch Your Steps
- Be Organised
- Be a Team Player
- Tim Berners Lee
- Find Flaws
- Ask for Help
- Get Practising

Think Like an Engineer
- What is an Engineer?
- Find a Problem
- State the Problem
- Imagine a Solution
- Charles K. Kao
- Brainstorm
- Don't be Scared
- Break it Down
- Margaret E. Knight
- Choose the Best Solution
- Draw Your Project
- Nikola Tesla
- Plan Your Project
- Build Your Project
- Don't be Discouraged
- Review Your Project
- Emily Warren Roebling
- Improve Your Project
- Recycle
- Awesome Engineers
- You Can Do It!

Think Like an Artist
- What is Art?
- Use Your Eyes
- Find the Beauty
- Michelangelo
- Connect and Combine
- Reuse Old Materials
- Learn from Earlier Artists
- Frida Kahlo
- Plan Carefully
- Practise Regularly
- Experiment
- Make Mistakes
- Review Your Work
- Wu Guanzhong
- Ask for Help
- Work with Others
- Give and Receive Feedback
- Georgia O'Keefe
- Set Yourself Goals
- Challenge Yourself
- Don't Expect Perfection

Think Like a Mathematician
- What do Mathematicians do?
- Be Logical
- Find the Proof
- Archimedes
- Solve Problems
- Think Visually
- Investigate
- Emmy Noether
- Try Working Backwards
- Mistakes are OK!
- Look for Patterns
- Terry Tao
- Break Codes
- Make a Plan
- Find the General Rule
- Be Resilient
- Sofya Kovalevskaya
- Put in the Practice
- Be Curious
- Work Together
- Maths is Everywhere

Think Like an Astronaut
- Travelling to Space
- Be Healthy and Fit
- Be Practical
- Neil Armstrong
- Make Good Decisions
- Improvise to Survive
- Change Your Perspective
- Valentina Tereshkova
- Floating Free
- Prepare to be Lonely
- Communicate
- Mae Jemison
- Take Care
- Be Curious and Observant
- Develop Your Piloting Skills
- Chris Hadfield
- Be a Teamworker
- Fly to the Moon
- Mission to Mars
- Navigating in Space
- Living in Space

WAYLAND
www.waylandbooks.co.uk

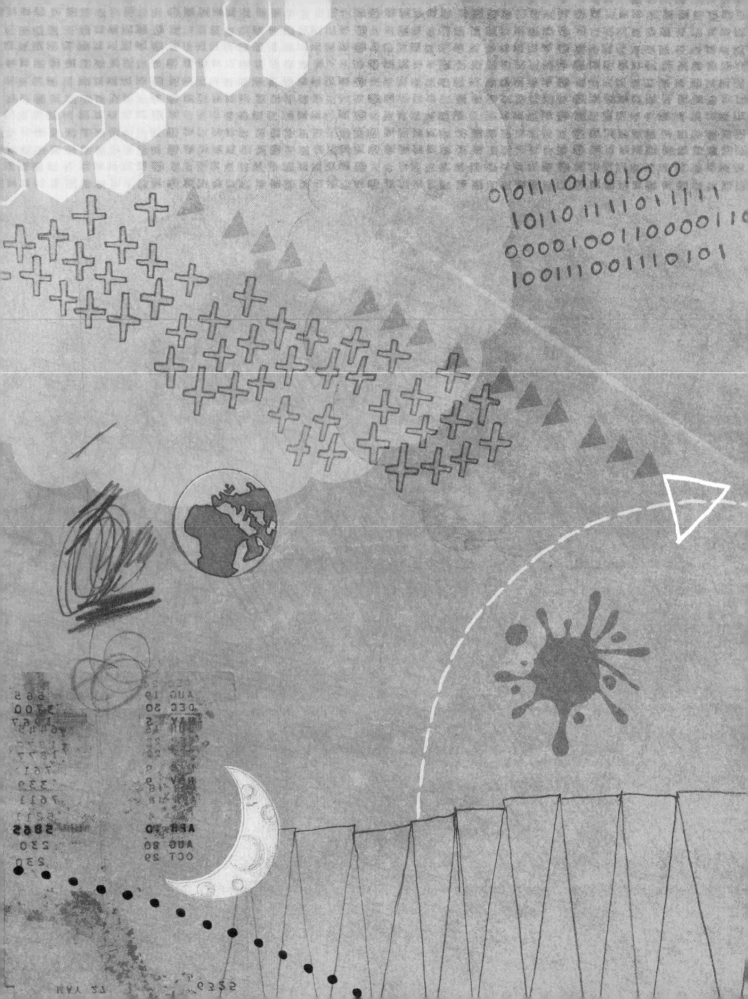